Algebra Tiles
for the
Overhead Projector

Hilde Howden

Cuisenaire Company of America, Inc.
10 Bank Street
White Plains, NY 10602

Contributing Editor: Lois Folsom

Production: Joshua M. Berger

Copyright© 1985, 1994 by
Cuisenaire® Company of America, Inc.
10 Bank Street, PO Box 5026
White Plains, NY, 10602-5026

3 4 5 6-BB-98 97 96 95

CONTENTS

INTRODUCTION

It is generally recognized that understanding the meaning of a mathematics concept, as opposed to merely performing the associated computation, is an essential element of true learning and achievement. Although research shows that modeling and visualization promote such understanding, algebra has traditionally been taught at the symbolic level. Not all algebraic concepts can be modeled with manipulatives, but the concrete-pictorial-symbolic sequence applies readily to the basic operations on polynomials, which encompasses a large part of the typical Algebra I course.

Modeling these operations is not a new idea. Algebra books sometimes introduce multiplication of binomials with one or two illustrations such as these:

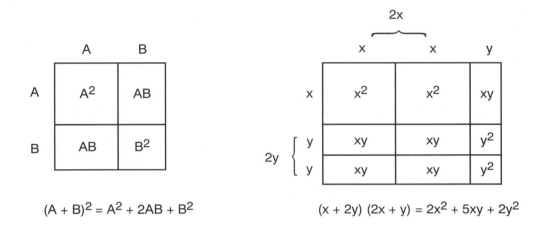

$$(A + B)^2 = A^2 + 2AB + B^2$$

$$(x + 2y)(2x + y) = 2x^2 + 5xy + 2y^2$$

As valuable as such illustrations may be, they are "too little, too late" for the student who has thought of variables only as symbols and has never used an area model to represent multiplication.

In the past, creative teachers who wished to extend this treatment used squares and rectangles cut from cardboard to represent the three types of areas shown in the figures above. More recently, Algebra Tiles in classroom sets have become commercially available.

Algebra Tiles are not tools, such as abaci or calculators, that do the "thinking" for us and supply the answer; they are concrete models of variables and/or integers that help us to explore concepts and to which we can attach the language of mathematics. That is, Algebra Tiles should be used as models to think from, to bridge the gap between a concept and the symbols used to record it algebraically.

Algebra Tiles for the Overhead Projector can be used as a teacher-directed supplement to student use of tiles or for introducing the idea of modeling by focusing the students' attention and having them "think along" with each demonstration.

Whether or not students have sets of tiles to work with, it is important for them to experience and become proficient in the draw-a-picture and see-a-mental-image stages before proceeding to the symbolic stage for each of the basic operations on polynomials in order to bond the various stages of development.

The purpose of this book is to serve as a guide for introducing tiles and integrating their use into a textbook-oriented course of study; a variety of Algebra I texts have been consulted to insure compatibility of teaching strategies. Suggestions in the guide draw heavily on the experiences of teachers in the Albuquerque Public Schools who, under the direction of Lois Folsom, an itinerant mathematics teacher in the district, have classroom-tested this use of tiles for many years. They have found the integrated approach preserves the continuity of the textbook development by eliminating the breaks and changes in focus that often result when separate instructional units are used. They have also found that the time spent incorporating the tiles is more than compensated for when understanding of concepts and student motivation eliminate the need for the usual review and reinforcement later in the course.

In each of the seven units in this guide, a concept is introduced on the concrete level and carried through the draw-a-picture and see-a-mental-image stages. Specific algebraic examples are given to illustrate the use of the tiles, and student exercises are included when it was found necessary to supplement the content of most textbooks. However, as evident from the Reinforcement, Assignment, and Extension features of each unit, the intent is for each stage of development to be used with textbook examples and exercises.

The time required for the individual units varies. Unit 1, Modeling Polynomials, is concerned only with concepts, no skills to be practiced, and can thus be taught in one session with assessment and extension in the following class period. The content of the other six units should be paced to coordinate with the corresponding development in your textbook.

Because of my strong conviction that Algebra Tiles should be used to model concepts, not as a tool for solving equations, the original edition of this guide purposefully avoided work with solving linear equations and with completing the square and derivation of the quadratic formula, both of which are algorithms for solving quadratic equations. However, at the urging of many teachers who have used Algebra Tiles in their classrooms, this extended edition of the guide includes two additional units that provide suggestions for using area models from which to think and talk about the underlying concepts of and relationships involved in completing the square and the quadratic formula. Also included are occasional notes, suggested by extensive use of Algebra Tiles with students and pre-service and inservice teachers.

Unit 1
MODELING POLYNOMIALS

In algebra, a variable such as x or y represents any member of some set, usually some number. If we let x represent the length of the side of the large blue square tile, then the area of the blue tile can be represented as x^2.

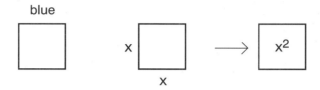

Similarly, if y represents the length of the side of the small yellow square tile, then y^2 represents its area, and xy represents the area of the green rectangular tile, since one of its dimensions is x and the other is y.

The lengths of the sides of the blue and yellow tiles are purposefully noncommensurable, unlike Base Ten Blocks and other similar products, to illustrate the most general condition of the variables they represent. That is, one variable is not necessarily a multiple of the other so that an x^2 tile cannot be exactly covered by xy tiles, nor can an xy tile be exactly covered by y^2 tiles.

Thus, we can use the tiles to model polynomials. For example,

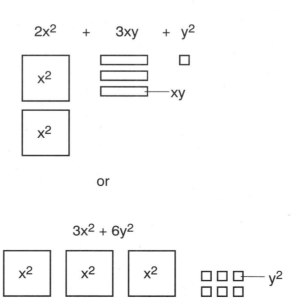

By assigning a negative value to each red tile, polynomials with negative terms can also be modeled.

Note: In the student set of tiles, one face of each tile is red. Thus, the faces of each tile represent a quantity and its additive inverse.

Use the tiles to model a variety of polynomials such as the following and similar examples from your textbook, until students feel comfortable with the tiles.

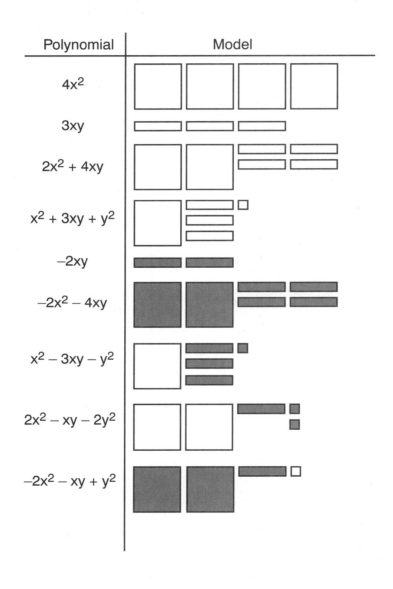

REINFORCEMENT

1. Project groups of tiles and have students identify the polynomials they represent. Point out that any two variables can be used to represent the dimensions of the blue and yellow tiles. Have the students state the variables they have chosen to use before identifying the polynomials.

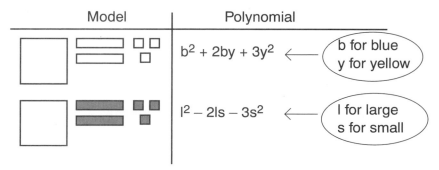

Note: One of the key components in the study of algebra is the concept of "variable" and the way variables are used. Using a variety of letters to represent variables, rather than limiting the choice to only x and y, gives a more comprehensive view of the concept of variable.

2. Have students draw a picture of the tile model for each of the following polynomials, or of polynomials taken from your textbook, and compare their drawings with the projected tile model.

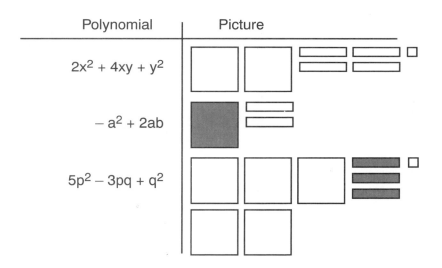

ASSIGNMENT

1. From your textbook, select several polynomials that can be modeled with the tiles and have students draw pictures of their models.

2. Ask each student to visualize (see a mental picture of) a group of five or more tiles and to draw a picture of it. After selecting and recording the variables that the lengths of the sides of the tiles represent, have the students express in algebraic form the polynomial represented by their groups of tiles. Tiles and the polynomials they represent can be projected for the class to share.

EXTENSION (Optional)

1. Ask students to use tiles to model like terms and unlike terms. Then ask students to describe the difference between like and unlike terms.

   Response: "Like terms have tile models with the same dimensions; unlike terms have tile models with unlike dimensions."

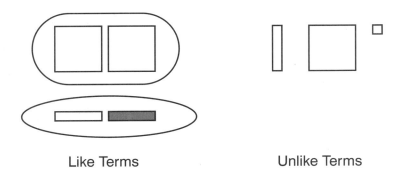

Like Terms	Unlike Terms

2. From your textbook, choose a polynomial that cannot be modeled by the algebra tiles. For example, $2x^2 + 3xy - 4yz + z^2$ or $x^3 + 2x^2y + xy^2 + y^3$. Ask the students why such polynomials cannot be modeled with the set of algebra tiles and what additional tiles would be needed to model such polynomials. Discuss with the students that a model is a typical form and that the set of tiles used on the overhead was designed to model the typical forms of polynomials studied in high school algebra.

   Response: "There are three variables in the polynomial $2x^2 + 3xy - 4yz + z^2$. Thus, in addition to the x^2, the xy, and the y^2 tiles in our set of tiles, we need z^2 tiles (square tiles whose sides each measure z) and yz tiles (rectangular tiles whose dimensions are y and z)."

   Note: You may wish to discuss three-dimensional models with your students. In the polynomial $x^3 + 2x^2y + xy^2 + y^3$ each of the terms is a third-degree term. Since we model a second-degree term as the measure, or area, of a two-dimensional tile, we can model a third-degree term as the measure, or volume, of a three-dimensional tile. That is, x^2 represents the area of a square tile whose dimensions are x and x; and x^3 can represent the volume of a cubical tile whose dimensions are x, x, and x. An x^2y term can represent the volume of a rectangular prism tile whose dimensions are x, x, and y. Likewise, y^3 can represent the volume of a cubical tile whose dimensions are y, y, and y. An xy^2 term can be represented by the volume of a rectangle prism tile whose dimensions are y, y, and x.

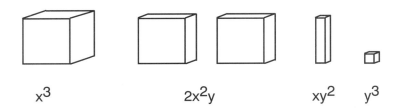

x^3	$2x^2y$	xy^2	y^3

Unit 2
THE ZERO PRINCIPLE

Compare these tiles.

Their similarities and differences represent similarities and differences in the quantities they model.

Since the tiles have the same dimensions, they represent like quantities; they have the same absolute value. But, as agreed earlier,

and

have opposite signs. When one is positive, the other is negative. Taken together, they cancel each other and form a model of zero.

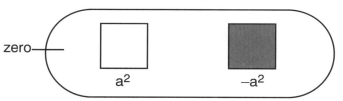

zero

a^2 $-a^2$

ZERO PRINCIPLE: Zero can be represented by any two like quantities with opposite signs.

There are many ways to represent zero.

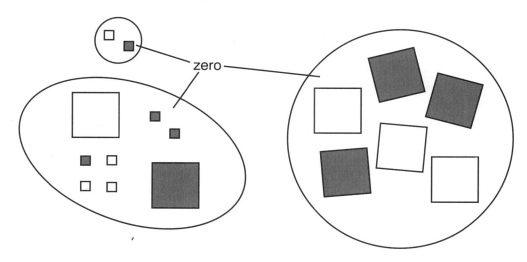

zero

Any two quantities that cancel each other to form zero are called *additive inverses* or *opposites.* Thus, any two tiles, or groups of tiles, that cancel each other are models of additive inverses.

As each of several random groups of tiles is displayed, have students identify whether the Zero Principle can be applied to form cancellations. Move the tiles that model additive inverses to the side and write the term(s) represented by the remaining tiles.

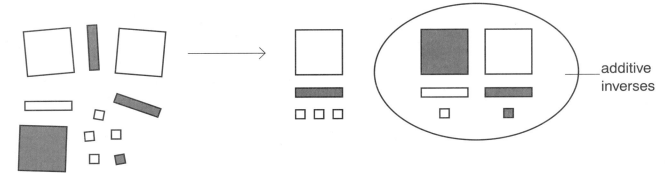

additive inverses

The Zero Principle can also be used to reinforce the properties of integers. Let the dimensions of a square tile be 1 and 1. Then the tile, whose area is 1, is the model of the integer 1. Its additive inverse is −1.

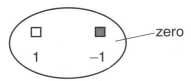

zero

1   −1

To model a polynomial such as $x^2 - 3x + 4$, which has a constant term, each side of one of the square tiles can be assigned the length of 1 unit, so that its area is 1 square unit. By letting the other square tile represent x^2, the rectangular tile represents x.

Thus, $x^2 - 3x + 4$ can be thought of as $x^2 + (-3x) + 4$ and modeled as

REINFORCEMENT

1. Select several polynomials of the form $ax^2 + bx + c$ from your textbook. As you model them with tiles, have students draw pictures of their models and check them against the projected tile models.

2. Ask students to write a definition of additive inverses in their own words and to illustrate the definition with a tile model. Discuss the various definitions that are submitted to reinforce both the model and symbolic representations.

3. Select a polynomial of the form $ax^2 + bxy + cy^2$ from your textbook. As you model it with tiles, have students draw a picture of its model and of the model of its additive inverse.

ASSIGNMENT

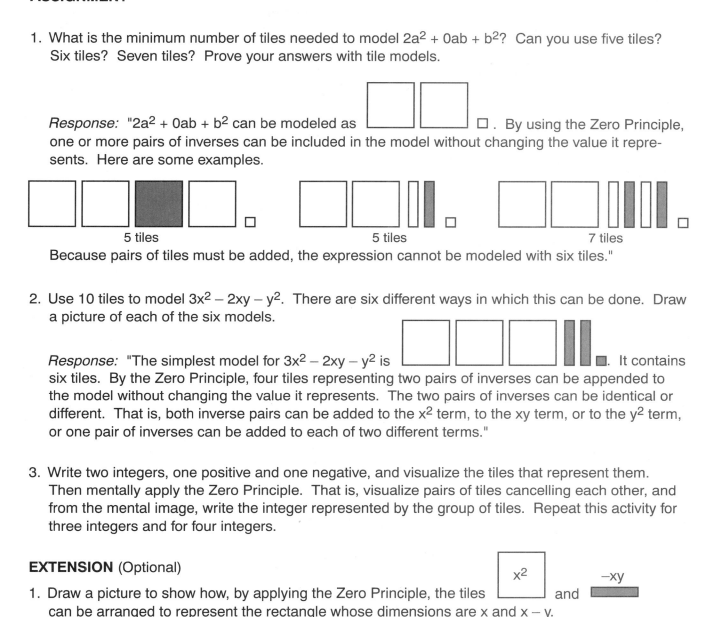

1. What is the minimum number of tiles needed to model $2a^2 + 0ab + b^2$? Can you use five tiles? Six tiles? Seven tiles? Prove your answers with tile models.

Response: "$2a^2 + 0ab + b^2$ can be modeled as ⬜⬜ ▫ . By using the Zero Principle, one or more pairs of inverses can be included in the model without changing the value it represents. Here are some examples.

    5 tiles   5 tiles   7 tiles

Because pairs of tiles must be added, the expression cannot be modeled with six tiles."

2. Use 10 tiles to model $3x^2 - 2xy - y^2$. There are six different ways in which this can be done. Draw a picture of each of the six models.

Response: "The simplest model for $3x^2 - 2xy - y^2$ is ⬜⬜⬜▮▮▪. It contains six tiles. By the Zero Principle, four tiles representing two pairs of inverses can be appended to the model without changing the value it represents. The two pairs of inverses can be identical or different. That is, both inverse pairs can be added to the x^2 term, to the xy term, or to the y^2 term, or one pair of inverses can be added to each of two different terms."

3. Write two integers, one positive and one negative, and visualize the tiles that represent them. Then mentally apply the Zero Principle. That is, visualize pairs of tiles cancelling each other, and from the mental image, write the integer represented by the group of tiles. Repeat this activity for three integers and for four integers.

EXTENSION (Optional)

1. Draw a picture to show how, by applying the Zero Principle, the tiles x^2 ⬜ and $-xy$ ▬ can be arranged to represent the rectangle whose dimensions are x and $x - y$.

Response: "Place the $-xy$ tile on the x^2 tile to show that part of its area is cancelled, leaving a rectangle whose dimensions are x and $x - y$."

2. Describe how these tiles can be arranged to model a square whose sides measure $x - y$. How many times is the Zero Principle applied in the model?

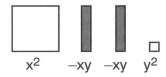

x^2 $\quad -xy$ $\quad -xy$ $\quad y^2$

Response: "Place the first $-xy$ tile on the x^2 tile as in Exercise 1. This leaves a rectangle whose dimensions are x and $x - y$.

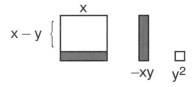

$x - y$ { $\quad$ x

$\qquad\qquad -xy \quad y^2$

Placing the second $-xy$ tile cancels more of the x^2 tile to form a square with dimensions $x - y$ and $x - y$, but it adds a $-y^2$ quantity.

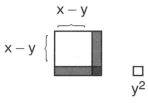

$x - y$ { $\quad$ $x - y$

$\qquad\qquad\qquad y^2$

The $-y^2$ quantity is cancelled by the y^2 tile. Thus the Zero Principle is applied three times."

Unit 3
ADDING AND SUBTRACTING POLYNOMIALS

To model addition of polynomials, you "put together" tiles that represent like terms, using the Zero Principle whenever possible.

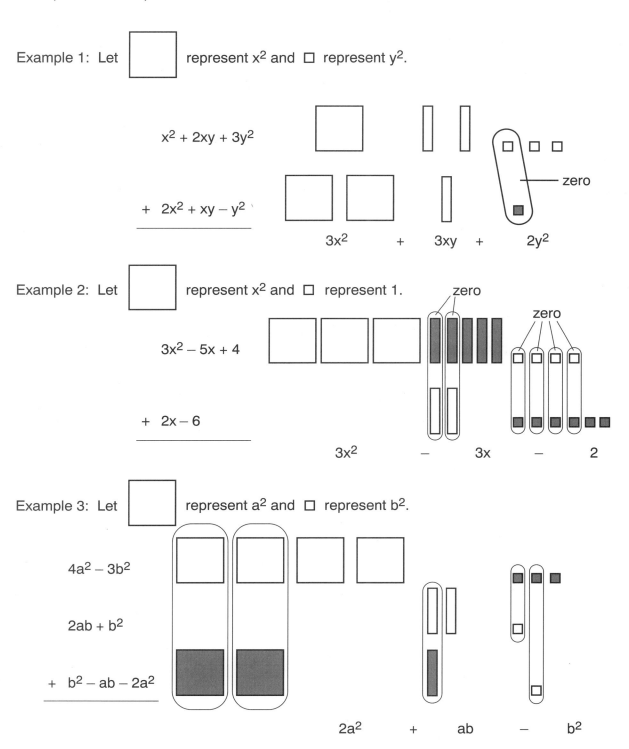

Example 1: Let ☐ represent x^2 and ☐ represent y^2.

$x^2 + 2xy + 3y^2$

$+ \; 2x^2 + xy - y^2$

$3x^2 \quad + \quad 3xy \quad + \quad 2y^2$

zero

Example 2: Let ☐ represent x^2 and ☐ represent 1.

$3x^2 - 5x + 4$

$+ \; 2x - 6$

$3x^2 \quad - \quad 3x \quad - \quad 2$

zero   zero

Example 3: Let ☐ represent a^2 and ☐ represent b^2.

$4a^2 - 3b^2$

$2ab + b^2$

$+ \; b^2 - ab - 2a^2$

$2a^2 \quad + \quad ab \quad - \quad b^2$

To model subtraction of polynomials, you "take away" tiles that represent terms of the subtrahend.

Example 1: Let represent x^2 and $\square$ represent y^2.

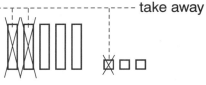

$$\begin{array}{r} 2x^2 + 5xy + 3y^2 \\ - \quad x^2 + 2xy + y^2 \\ \hline x^2 + 3xy + 2y^2 \end{array}$$

Example 2: Let represent x^2 and $\square$ represent 1.

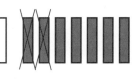

$$\begin{array}{r} 3x^2 - 7x + 4 \\ - \quad x^2 - 2x + 2 \\ \hline 2x^2 - 5x + 2 \end{array}$$

The "take away" method works when there are tiles to take away, but consider this example.

$$\begin{array}{r} 2x^2 - 7x + 4 \\ - \quad x^2 + 2x + 2 \end{array}$$

There are no x tiles to take away, only –x tiles. But we can provide as many x tiles as we need by applying the Zero Principle. Since we need two x tiles, we can represent

$2x^2 - 7x + 4$ as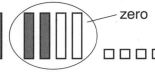

Now we can take away the tiles that represent the subtrahend $x^2 + 2x + 2$, and count the remaining tiles to determine the difference.

$$x^2 \qquad - \qquad 9x \qquad + \qquad 2$$

Here is another example that requires us to use the Zero Principle.

$$3x^2 + 5xy - y^2 - (x^2 - 2xy + y^2)$$

Let [ ] represent x^2 and □ represent y^2. Then the model

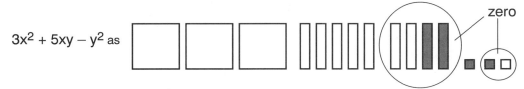

$3x^2 + 5xy - y^2$ is

Since we need to take away two $-xy$ tiles and one y^2 tile, we can represent

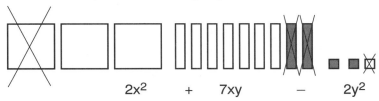

$3x^2 + 5xy - y^2$ as

Now we can take away the tiles that represent $x^2 - 2xy + y^2$ and count the tiles that are left.

$$2x^2 \quad + \quad 7xy \quad - \quad 2y^2$$

The algorithm for subtraction is generally stated in either of two ways.

> To subtract a quantity, change its sign and add.
>
> or
>
> To subtract a quantity, add its additive inverse.

Applying the Zero Principle to tile models illustrates the rationale for each of these methods.

Let [ ] represent x^2 and □ represent 1.

Zero Principle Method

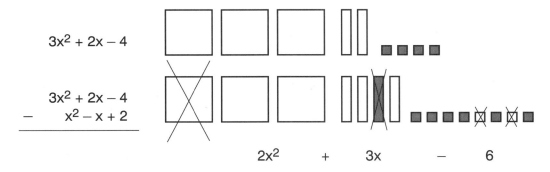

$3x^2 + 2x - 4$

$3x^2 + 2x - 4$
$- \quad x^2 - x + 2$

$$2x^2 \quad + \quad 3x \quad - \quad 6$$

Additive Inverse Method

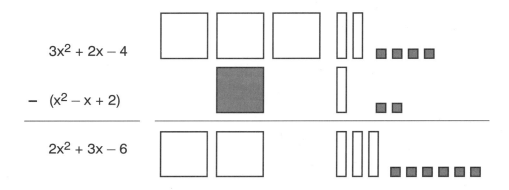

$3x^2 + 2x - 4$

$-\ (x^2 - x + 2)$

$2x^2 + 3x - 6$

Note: Color designation to indicate additive inverse is an asset in modeling expressions such as xy − 2 as xy + (−2), which identifies addition and subtraction as inverse operations. Also, this strategy eliminates the need to make a big deal about the two uses of the negative sign: to indicate the subtraction operation and to identify negative (additive inverse) quantities.

REINFORCEMENT

1. As you model several addition of polynomial exercises from your textbook, have students draw pictures of the models and check them against the projected models.

2. Select several subtraction of polynomial exercises from your textbook. Have students direct you in modeling each exercise, first using the Zero Principle Method and then the Additive Inverse Method.

ASSIGNMENT

1. From your textbook, select several addition of polynomial exercises. Draw pictures of their models to find each sum.

2. Select several subtraction of polynomial exercises from your textbook, some in vertical format and some in horizontal format. Draw pictures of their models to find each difference by both the Zero Principle Method and the Additive Inverse Method.

3. Draw a picture of any two groups of tiles and identify the quantity each kind of tile represents. Write the polynomial that is modeled by each group and identify one group as the minuend and the other as the subtrahend. Write a detailed description of how a tile model would be used to find their difference using the Zero Principle Method.

EXTENSION (Optional)

1. Use these pictures of the tile models of the sum and difference of two polynomials to identify the polynomials. The ☐ represents x^2 and ☐ represents y^2.

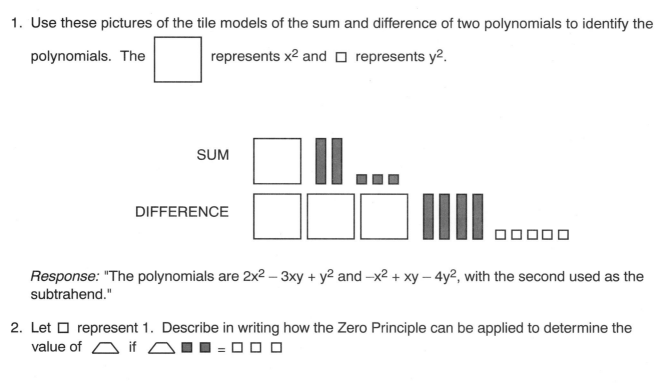

Response: "The polynomials are $2x^2 - 3xy + y^2$ and $-x^2 + xy - 4y^2$, with the second used as the subtrahend."

2. Let ☐ represent 1. Describe in writing how the Zero Principle can be applied to determine the value of △ if △ ■ ■ = ☐ ☐ ☐

Note: In modeling equations to be solved, Pattern Blocks, rather than Algebra Tiles, are recommended for representing the variable to conform to the incommensurable nature of the tiles and to avoid confusion concerning color distinction in the tiles.

Unit 4
MULTIPLYING POLYNOMIALS

The tile model for multiplying polynomials builds on the area concept of multiplication, which is an inherent feature of the tiles themselves. Just as the tile whose dimensions are identified as x and y represents the quantity xy, the area of the tile, so the quantity represented by a rectangular array of tiles represents the area of the array.

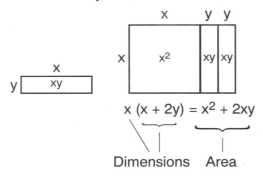

$$x(x + 2y) = x^2 + 2xy$$

Dimensions   Area

Note how the array models the Distributive Property of Multiplication.

To multiply 2x by x + 5y, let ☐ represent x^2 and ☐ represent y^2.

Use the sides of the tiles to mark off the dimensions 2x and x + 5y along two perpendicular lines.

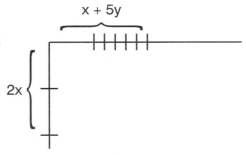

Note: Marking off lengths of sides of tiles along the multiplication/division frame rather than placing tiles along the frame helps to differentiate between linear and area measure.

Then form the rectangular array of tiles that has these dimensions. By counting the x^2 tiles and the xy tiles in the array, we see that

$$2x(x + 5y) = 2x^2 + 10xy.$$

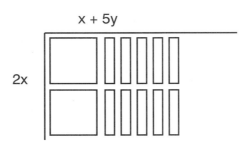

Note: Although tiles in the rectangular arrays will abut, including space between them in drawings, as is done here, makes the picture easier to read and conforms to the dot and line drawings students may wish to use, i.e., ⬜⬜!!! .

A similar model can be made for the product $(x + 2)(x + 3)$. Let ⬜ represent x^2 and □ represent 1.

Mark off the dimensions and form the rectangular array.

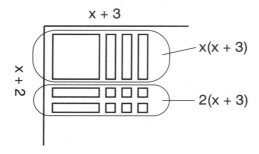

Notice that the Distributive Property is used twice. Also notice how the model illustrates the traditional multiplication algorithm.

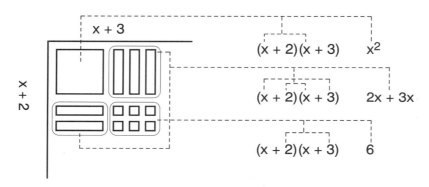

$(x + 2)(x + 3)$	x^2
$(x + 2)(x + 3)$	$2x + 3x$
$(x + 2)(x + 3)$	6

Use the tiles to model multiplication of a monomial and a binomial and of two binomials, with all terms positive, taken from your textbook. Do sufficient examples to insure that students can successfully draw pictures of the models.

Now consider a product in which one of the terms is negative, such as $x(x - 2)$. Using ⬜ to represent x^2 and ■ to represent -1, the model can take either of two forms.

Additive Inverse Model

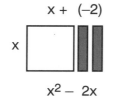

Zero Principle Model

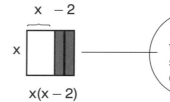

Place the two $-xy$ tiles on the x^2 tile to show that part of it is cancelled.

Each of the models has advantages. In the Additive Inverse Model, it is easy to count the tiles in the array and to express the product represented by the array as a sum, which illustrates the use of the Distributive Property. The Zero Principle Model illustrates the factors x and x − 2 as dimensions of the product rectangle. It also models the properties of the signs of the product of a negative and a positive number and of two negative numbers. Until these properties are established, we will use a combination of the two models. Later we will use the Additive Inverse Model exclusively.

Example 1: One Negative Term

To find the product of x + y and 2x − y, let ☐ represent x^2 and ☐ represent y^2. Use the sides of the tiles to mark off the factors along two perpendicular lines.

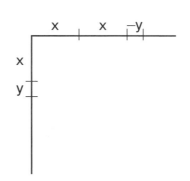

Fill in the rectangular area with tiles. In order to form the rectangular array of tiles, we need two x^2 tiles, two xy tiles, one −xy tile, and one other tile. Is this last tile a y^2 tile or a $-y^2$ tile?

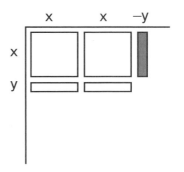

The Zero Principle Model helps to answer this question. Placing the −xy tile on the x^2 tile highlights 2x − y as a dimension of the rectangle and shows that the missing tile must represent $-y^2$ to give a rectangular array.

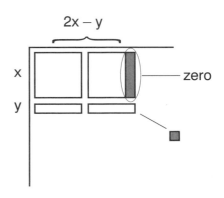

Now when the tiles are again arranged according to the Additive Inverse Model, the various tiles in the array can be counted to determine the product.

Note: The product of y and −y is $-y^2$.

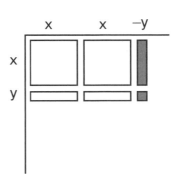

This model also verifies the sign property for multiplying a negative number and a positive number.

> The product of a negative number and a positive number is a negative number.

Example 2: Two Negative Terms

Consider the product $(x - 2)(x - 1)$.

Let [ ] represent x^2 and □ represent 1.

Use the sides of these tiles to mark off the dimensions of the tile array. Again we can place the x^2 tile and the $-x$ tiles, but to determine which tiles are needed to complete the rectangular array, we use the Zero Principle Model.

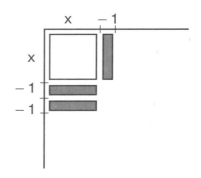

By placing the two $-x$ tiles horizontally on the x^2 tile, the $x - 2$ dimension is established.

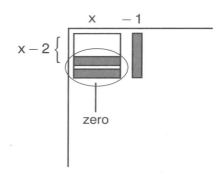

When the $-x$ tile is placed vertically on the x^2 tile to establish the $x - 1$ dimension, it overlaps part of the area (or quantity) already cancelled. That is, we now have an extra negative quantity, namely -2, which can be cancelled by two 1 tiles.

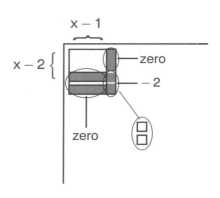

When all these tiles (the x^2 tile, the three $-x$ tiles, and the two 1 tiles) are arranged according to the Additive Inverse Model, the rectangular array is complete, the product is seen to be $x^2 - 3x + 2$, and the sign property for multiplying two negative numbers is verified.

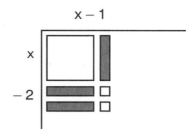

x − 1

The product of two negative numbers is a positive number.

Note: The Zero Principle Model focuses on the rectangle whose dimensions represent the given factors, while the Additive Inverse Model focuses on the tiles that are needed to complete the rectangular array and verifies the sign property for multiplying two negative numbers.

As you model examples of multiplication of two binomials from your textbook, point out why the product is a trinomial and the nature of each of the three terms, so that students are able to first draw pictures of the models and then to visualize the models without drawing their pictures.

Special products, such as squares of binomials, take on added meaning when their models are examined.

For example, the model of $(x + 3)^2$ is a square array, since each of its dimensions represents the same quantity. Examination of the model shows that the 1 tiles are arranged in a square array and the x tiles are arranged in two identical rectangles.

$$(x + 3)^2 = x^2 + 2(3x) + 3^2$$

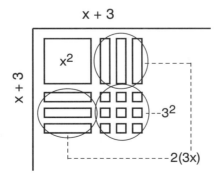

Consider $(3x - 4)^2$.

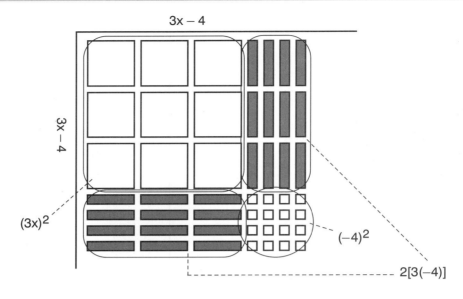

$$(3x - 4)^2 = 9x^2 - 24x + 16$$

The model illustrates that the square of any binomial of the form $dx + e$ must have the same pattern.

$$(dx + e)^2 = (dx)^2 + 2(dx)(e) + e^2.$$

Note: Recognizing this pattern is important for deriving the quadratic formula, which is dependent upon the process of completing the square.

REINFORCEMENT

1. As you model several multiplication of binomials exercises from your textbook, have students draw pictures of the models and check them against the projected models. Use the Additive Inverse Model to verify the dimensions of the product rectangle.

2. Project several rectangular arrays of tiles such as the following.

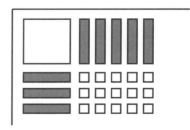

Ask students to identify the area of each in two forms: as a polynomial expression in standard form and as the product of two polynomials.

ASSIGNMENT

1. Draw a picture of the model for multiplying $(x + 3)(2x - 1)$. Then reverse the dimensions of the product rectangle. That is, draw a picture of the model for multiplying $(2x - 1)(x + 3)$. What conclusion can you make from the two drawings? What property have you verified?

2. Complete each picture to determine the binomials being multiplied.

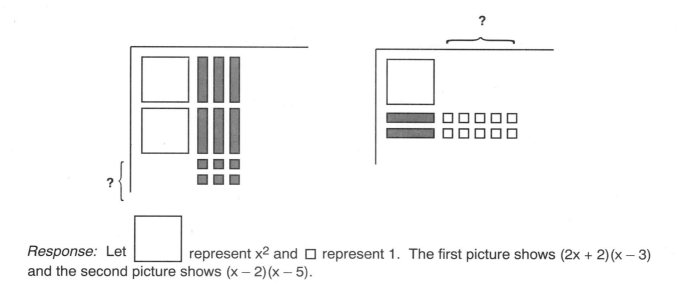

Response: Let [ ] represent x^2 and □ represent 1. The first picture shows $(2x + 2)(x - 3)$ and the second picture shows $(x - 2)(x - 5)$.

3. Draw a picture of the model for each multiplication of polynomials exercise assigned from your text-book.

4. Draw a picture of the model for multiplying 13 and 22, using [grid] to represent 100 and □ to represent 1.

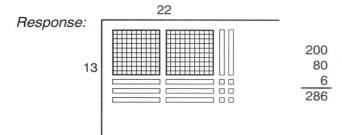

Response:

```
      200
       80
        6
      286
```

5. If you were designing a set of tiles to model the product of $(x + 4)$ and $(y + 2)$, describe the tiles you would need to include. Then draw a picture of the model for multiplying $(x + 4)$ and $(y + 2)$.

Response: "You would need xy tiles, y tiles, x tiles, and 1 tiles."

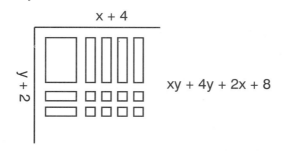

$xy + 4y + 2x + 8$

EXTENSION (Optional)

1. The area of a product rectangle in a multiplication model is $4x^2 + 9x + 2$. Draw a picture of the product rectangle showing the individual tiles. Then determine its dimensions.

Response:

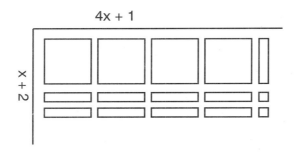

2. Describe the kinds of tiles and list the numbers of each kind of tile that would be needed to build a model of the product $(x + 1)(x + 1)(x + 1)$. Draw a picture of the model.

Response: Tiles needed: one x^3 tile, three x^2 tiles, three x tiles, and one 1 tile.

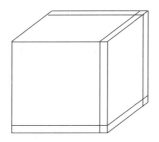

Unit 5
DIVIDING AND FACTORING TRINOMIALS

Tile models of multiplication, division, and factorization of polynomials show how the three operations are related. Consider the models of binomials of the form (ax + b) and (cx + d) and their product.

In multiplication, the dimensions of the product rectangle are given and its area is to be determined.

$$cx + d$$

$$ax + b \quad | \quad ?$$

In division, the area of the product rectangle and one of its dimensions are given and the other dimension is to be determined.

$$?$$

$$ax + b \quad | \quad acx^2 + (ad + bc)x + bd$$

In factoring, the area of the product rectangle is given and both dimensions are to be determined.

$$?$$

$$? \quad | \quad acx^2 + (ad + bc)x + bd$$

For example, to model $(x^2 + 6x + 8) \div (x + 4)$, one x^2 tile, six x tiles, and eight 1 tiles are arranged in a rectangular array that has x + 4 as one of its dimensions.

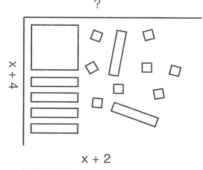

From their experience with modeling multiplication, students will see that a rectangular array can be formed by placing the x^2 tile at the upper left of the array, the 1 tiles at the lower right, and the x tiles at the lower left and upper right.

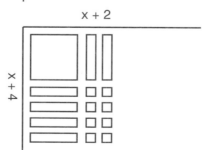

Students' attention may need to be directed to the application of the sign property for multiplying two negative quantities when the last term of the product trinomial, written in standard form $ax^2 + bx + c$, is positive and the middle term is negative. For example, consider

$$(x^2 - 4x + 3) \div (x - 1).$$

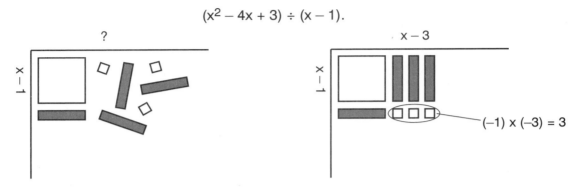

Sometimes there are too few tiles designated by the given trinomial to establish the dimension specified by the divisor. In such cases, the Zero Principle must be applied.

Example 1

To divide $x^2 + x - 6$ by $x + 3$, select one x^2 tile, one x tile, and six -1 tiles. Use the x^2 tile and the shorter side of the x tile to mark off the $x + 3$ dimension. Notice that two more x tiles are needed to establish the $x + 3$ dimension.

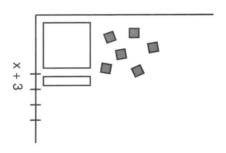

They can be added if two $-x$ tiles are also added.

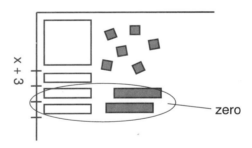

Now the two $-x$ tiles and the six -1 tiles can be arranged to complete the rectangular array whose dimensions are $x + 3$ and $x - 2$.

Thus, $(x^2 + x - 6) \div (x + 3) = x - 2$.

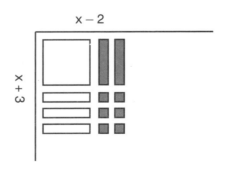

Example 2
Use a tile model to divide $x^2 - x - 2$ by $x - 2$.

Select the tiles indicated by the dividend.

An additional $-x$ tile needs to be added.

Now the tiles can be arranged in an array.

The quotient $x + 1$ can be read from the model. That is, $(x^2 - x - 2) \div (x - 2) = x + 1$.

The experience of drawing pictures of tile models for division of polynomials prepares students for modeling factoring, which can be thought of as determining both dimensions of a given product rectangle when only its area is given.

For example, to factor $x^2 + 7x + 6$, select the tiles that represent the three given terms.

Knowing that the x^2 tile is ordinarily placed at the upper left in the array and that the 1 tiles are placed at the lower right presents a problem-solving situation: how to place the 1 tiles to accommodate the seven x tiles.

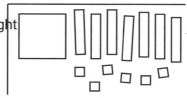

There are two options for arranging the 1 tiles to make a rectangular array: 2 by 3 or 1 by 6

Option 1

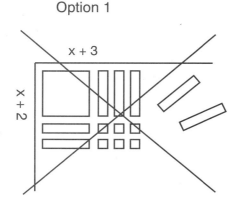

Option 2

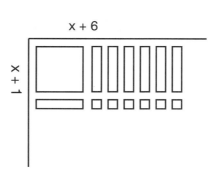

The 2 by 3 option requires only five x tiles to complete the product rectangle, which does not meet the condition established by the given trinomial $x^2 + 7x + 6$.

The 1 by 6 option requires seven x tiles to complete the product rectangle, which satisfies the condition established by the given trinomial $x^2 + 7x + 6$.

The factors $x + 1$ and $x + 6$ can be read from the model that satisfies the given condition. They are the conditions of the rectangular array. Thus, $x^2 + 7x + 6 = (x + 1)(x + 6)$.

Note how the thinking process used in forming the model illustrates the thinking used in applying the traditional factoring algorithm. For example, consider the factors of $x^2 + 6x + 8$. You know that each factor must contain an x to give the leading term of the trinomial.

$x^2 + 6x + 8$ (x   ) (x   )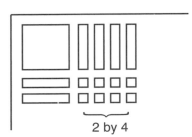

The product of the second terms in the factors must be 8. We have two options: 1 x 8 and 2 x 4.

Option 1	Option 2
(x + 1) (x + 8)	(x + 2) (x + 4)
Does not satisfy condition on x term.	Satisfies condition on x term.

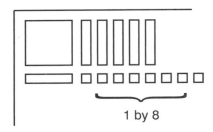

1 by 8

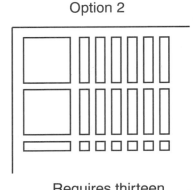

2 by 4

Therefore, $x^2 + 6x + 8 = (x + 2)(x + 4)$

When the coefficient of x^2 is different from 1, more options must be considered.

For example, to factor $2x^2 + 7x + 6$ by modeling, we must consider the placement of the two x^2 tiles as well as the placement of the six 1 tiles. Thus, there are four options to consider.

Option 1

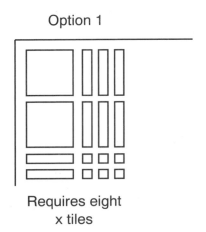

Requires eight
x tiles

Option 2

Requires thirteen
x tiles

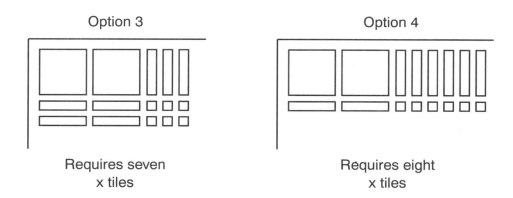

Option 3

Option 4

Requires seven
x tiles

Requires eight
x tiles

Since seven x tiles are required, the model for factoring $2x^2 + 7x + 6$ is option 3, the rectangular array with dimensions $x + 2$ and $2x + 3$.

$$2x^2 + 7x + 6 = (x + 2)(2x + 3)$$

2x + 3

x + 2

Example 3

Use a tile model to factor $2x^2 + 5x - 3$.

There are only two different array options, since options 3 and 4 are repeats of the first two arrays.

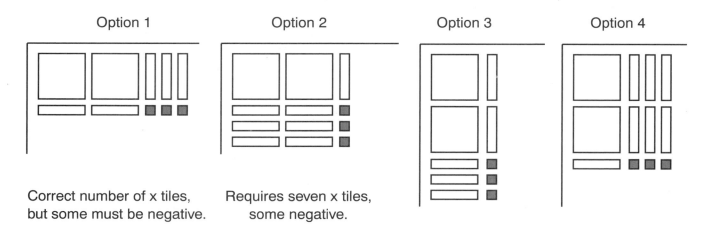

Option 1

Option 2

Option 3

Option 4

Correct number of x tiles,
but some must be negative.

Requires seven x tiles,
some negative.

The -1 tiles are a signal that the array must contain $-x$ tiles. Tiles can be added by applying the Zero Principle.

There is no space for additional x tiles in the first array (option 1), but there is space in the second array (option 2).

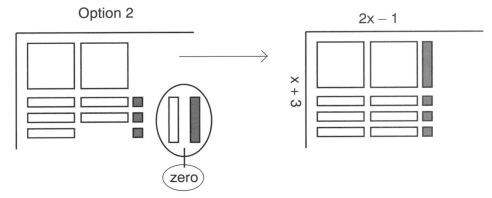

Option 2

2x − 1

zero

Thus, the factors of $2x^2 + 5x - 3$ are $x + 3$ and $2x - 1$.

When the polynomial to be factored has the form $(ax)^2 - b^2$, it is the difference of two squares, and all the x tiles necessary to represent its model must be added to applying the Zero Principle.

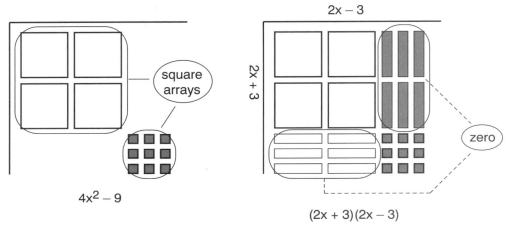

square arrays

$4x^2 - 9$

2x − 3

zero

$(2x + 3)(2x - 3)$

REINFORCEMENT

1. As you model division and factoring exercises from your textbook, have students draw pictures of their models and check them against the projections of the tile models.

2. The table shows the number of each of two of the three types of tiles contained in a rectangular array of tiles. The number of the third type of tile is missing. As array options for each set of table entries is projected, discuss with the students the possible value(s) for the missing entry.

x^2 tiles	x tiles	1 tiles
1 positive	?	9 positive
1 positive	6 positive	?
2 positive	7 positive	?
1 positive	?	6 positive
?	5 positive	2 negative
?	1 negative	1 negative

ASSIGNMENT

1. Draw a picture of the model of each division and factoring exercise assigned from your textbook.

2. Use a drawing of the factoring model to determine the missing term when each trinomial is the square of a binomial.

    a. $x^2 +$ ☐ $+ 49$ b. $x^2 + 12x +$ ☐

    c. $x^2 -$ ☐ $+ 36y^2$ d. $4x^2 - 4x +$ ☐

3. Write the trinomial whose factoring model is an array that contains the given tiles.

    a. One x^2 tile, three x tiles, three $-x$ tiles, and nine -1 tiles

    b. Four x^2 tiles, two xy tiles, two $-xy$ tiles, and one $-y^2$ tile

4. List the tiles contained in the factoring model of each polynomial.

    a. $x^2 - 16$ b. $9x^2 - 25$

    c. $4x^2 - 9y^2$ d. $x^2 - 81y^2$

EXTENSION (Optional)

1. The polynomial $x^2 + 6x + 4xy + 4y^2 + 12y + 9$ is the square of a trinomial. Make a drawing of its model to determine the trinomial.

    Response: The trinomial is $x + 2y + 3$.

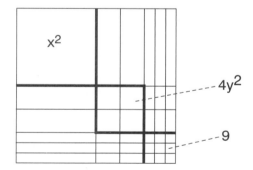

2. The polynomial $x^3 + 6x^2 + 12x + 8$ is the cube of a binomial. Use the sketch of its model to determine its binomial factors. Then show that your answer is correct.

    Response: The factors are $x + 2$, $x + 2$, and $x + 2$.

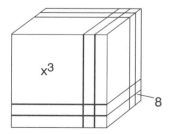

UNIT 6
Square Trinomials

Trinomials of the form $ax^2 + bx + c$, whose tile models can be arranged as a square array, are called square trinomials.

Each of these tile arrays is the model of a square trinomial.

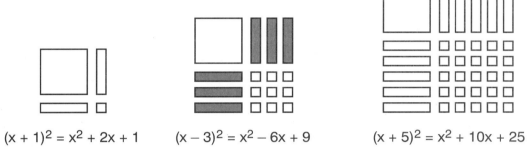

$(x + 1)^2 = x^2 + 2x + 1$ $(x - 3)^2 = x^2 - 6x + 9$ $(x + 5)^2 = x^2 + 10x + 25$

Compare the factor form and the sum form of each trinomial with the number of each type of tile in its model. Notice the pattern for each trinomial and its model.

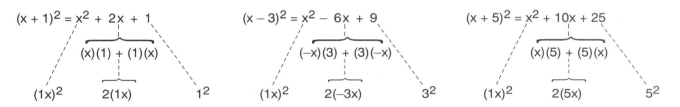

Note how the middle term is related to both the first and third terms. It is twice the product of their square roots. Also note that the first and third terms are always represented by a square array.

These square arrays illustrate the same pattern.

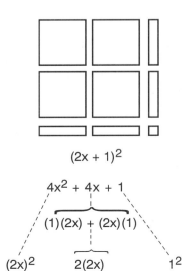

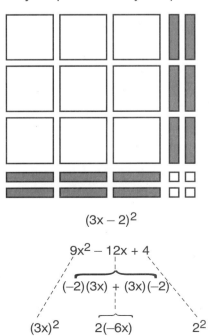

$(2x + 1)^2$

$4x^2 + 4x + 1$

$(1)(2x) + (2x)(1)$

$(2x)^2 \qquad 2(2x) \qquad 1^2$

$(3x - 2)^2$

$9x^2 - 12x + 4$

$(-2)(3x) + (3x)(-2)$

$(3x)^2 \qquad 2(-6x) \qquad 2^2$

Any trinomial that satisfies this pattern is a square trinomial, and conversely, any trinomial that does not satisfy this pattern is not a square trinomial. For example, $2x^2 + 2\sqrt{2}x + 1$ and $3x^2 + 2\sqrt{15}x + 5$ are square trinomials. Such square trinomials, whose first and last terms are not both perfect squares, are best represented by area models.

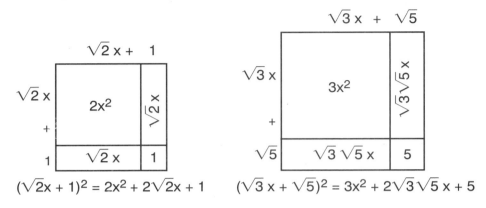

$(\sqrt{2}x + 1)^2 = 2x^2 + 2\sqrt{2}x + 1$ $(\sqrt{3}x + \sqrt{5})^2 = 3x^2 + 2\sqrt{3}\sqrt{5}x + 5$

Notice how the dimensions of the two square regions impact on the dimensions of the two rectangular regions.

If $7x^2 + bx + 3$ is a square trinomial, b must be $2\sqrt{7}\sqrt{3}$.

If $5x^2 + 2\sqrt{10}x + c$ is a square trinomial, c must be $(\frac{1}{2}\frac{2\sqrt{10}}{\sqrt{5}})^2$ or 2.

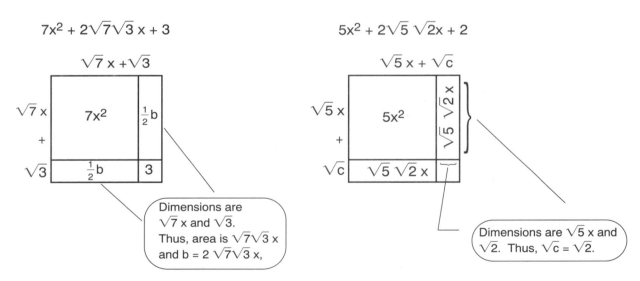

When $ax^2 + bx + c$ is a square trinomial, it can be represented by the following area model.

Since the dimensions of each of its two rectangular regions are $\sqrt{a}x$ and $\sqrt{c}$, the area $\frac{1}{2}bx$ must be equal to $\sqrt{a}\sqrt{c}x$, so that b is equal to $2\sqrt{a}\sqrt{c}$ and c is equal to $\frac{b^2}{4a}$. That is:

$$ax^2 + bx + c = (\sqrt{a}x + \sqrt{c})^2$$

$$ax^2 + bx + c = ax^2 + 2\sqrt{a}\sqrt{c}x + c$$

$$b = 2\sqrt{a}\sqrt{c}$$

and

$$b = 2\sqrt{a}\sqrt{c}$$

$$\frac{b}{2\sqrt{a}} = \sqrt{c}$$

$$\left(\frac{b}{2\sqrt{a}}\right)^2 = (\sqrt{c})^2$$

$$\frac{b^2}{4a} = c$$

REINFORCEMENT

1. Ask students to describe, in their own words, the pattern among the terms in any square trinomial.

2. Select several trinomial squares from your textbook. As you model them with tiles, have students draw pictures of their models and check them against the projected tile models to verify the pattern.

ASSIGNMENT

1. Select exercises from your textbook, similar to the following, that require students to supply a missing term of a square trinomial. Have them make tile models to identify the missing term.
   a. $x^2 + 8x + \boxed{}$　　　b. $p^2 - 30p + \boxed{}$　　　c. $s^2 + 3s + \boxed{}$
   d. $4y^2 + 12y + \boxed{}$　　　e. $9x^2 - 6x + \boxed{}$　　　f. $2x^2 + 3x + \boxed{}$

2. Use a tile model to explain why either of two terms can be added to each of these binomials to make a trinomial square.
   a. $q^2 + 49$　　　　　　b. $9p^2 + 1$　　　　　　c. $9z^2 + 16$

3. Ask students to classify several trinomials, such as the following, as square trinomials or not-square trinomials, and to justify their answers.
   a. $x^2 + 6x + 9$　　b. $y^2 + 6y + 36$　　c. $p^2 - 8p + 16$　　d. $x^2 + 4x + 64$
   e. $q^2 - 10q - 25$　　f. $9x^2 + 12x + 4$　　g. $16y^2 + 40y + 25$　　h. $4x^2 - 6x + 9$

4. Draw an area model of each of the following square trinomials and label the area of each of its four regions.
   a. $5y^2 + 4\sqrt{5}y + 4$　　　　b. $x^2 + 2\sqrt{7}x + 7$　　　　c. $2p^2 + 2\sqrt{6}p + 3$

EXTENSION (Optional)

1. Draw an area model for each of the following squares of binomials and express each in trinomial form ($ax^2 + bx + c$).
   a. $(x - 5)^2$　　　　　　b. $(2x + 3)^2$　　　　　　c. $(4x + 7)^2$

2. For each square trinomial in Exercise 1, verify the following relationships between b, the coefficient of the x term, and c, the constant term: $b = 2\sqrt{a}\sqrt{c}$ and $c = \frac{b^2}{4a}$.

UNIT 7
QUADRATIC EQUATION MODELS

If two squares have the same area, then they have the same dimensions.

$$(x + 2)^2 = 25 \quad \text{and} \quad x + 2 = \sqrt{25}$$

This relationship can be used to solve quadratic equations.

$$x^2 - 2x + 1 = 9 \qquad\qquad 4x^2 - 20x + 25 = 0$$

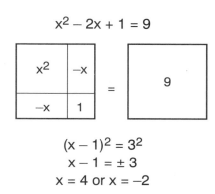

$$(x - 1)^2 = 3^2$$
$$x - 1 = \pm 3$$
$$x = 4 \text{ or } x = -2$$

When we replace x by either 4 or −2, we see that both sides of the equation have the same value.

$$(2x - 5)^2 = 0$$
$$2x - 5 = 0$$
$$x = \frac{5}{2}$$

When we replace x by $\frac{5}{2}$, we see that both sides of the equation have the same value.

Suppose we have a quadratic equation, such as $x^2 - 6x - 7 = 0$, in which the trinomial is not a square. We can still use the relationship by a process called completing the square. Visualize the two sides of the equation as equal areas.

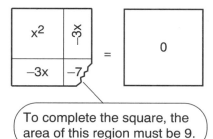

To complete the square, the area of this region must be 9.

The region on the left is not square, but by applying the Zero Principle and then adding 9, we can make it square. Of course, this alters its area, so we must alter the area of the square region on the right in the same way.

Area Model   Algebraic Record

1. Apply the Zero Principle.

x^2	$-3x$
$-3x$	

$=$ | 7 |

$$x^2 - 6x = 7$$

2. Complete the square.

x^2	$-3x$
$-3x$	9

$=$ | 16 |

$$x^2 - 6x + 9 = 16$$

3. Determine the dimensions of each square.
   Equate the dimensions and solve for x.

$x - 3$ 4 or -4

x^2	$-3x$
$-3x$	9

$=$ | 16 |

$$x - 3 = \pm 4$$
$$x = 7 \text{ or } -1$$

Thus, x is equal to either 7 or -1. By substituting these values in the original equation, we can verify that they satisfy the original equation, and are its solutions.

The completing-the-square method can also be used to solve quadratic equations in which the leading coefficient is different from 1, such as $3x^2 + 5x - 2 = 0$.

Visualize the two sides of the equation as equal areas.

$3x^2$	$\frac{5}{2}x$
$\frac{5}{2}x$	-2

$=$ | 0 |

$$3x^2 + 5x - 2 = 0$$

Area Model   Algebraic Record

1. Apply the Zero Principle.

$3x^2$	$\frac{5}{2}x$
$\frac{5}{2}x$	

$=$

2

$3x^2 + 5x = 2$

2. Complete the square.

Note how the area model helps by focusing on the dimensions of the rectangular regions.

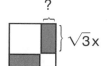

Since $(\sqrt{3}\,x)(?) = \frac{5}{2}x$, the width of the rectangular region must be $\frac{5}{2\sqrt{3}}$

and the area of the small square region must be $(\frac{5}{2\sqrt{3}})^2$ or $\frac{25}{12}$.

$3x^2$	$\frac{5}{2}x$
$\frac{5}{2}x$	$\frac{25}{12}$

$=$

$2 + \frac{25}{12}$

$3x^2 + 5x + \dfrac{25}{12} = 2 + \dfrac{25}{12}$

3. Determine the dimensions of each square.
   Equate the dimensions and solve for x.

$$\sqrt{3}x + \frac{5}{2\sqrt{3}} \qquad \frac{7}{2\sqrt{3}} \text{ or } -\frac{7}{2\sqrt{3}}$$

$3x^2$	$\frac{5}{2}x$
$\frac{5}{2}x$	$\frac{25}{12}$

$=$

$\frac{49}{12}$

$$\sqrt{3}\,x + \frac{5}{2\sqrt{3}} = \pm\frac{7}{2\sqrt{3}}$$

$$\sqrt{3}\,x = -\frac{5}{2\sqrt{3}} \pm \frac{7}{2\sqrt{3}}$$

$$\sqrt{3}\,x = \frac{-5 \pm 7}{2\sqrt{3}}$$

$$x = -2 \text{ or } +\frac{1}{3}$$

Substituting these values in the original equation verifies that they are its solutions.

$$3x^2 + 5x - 2 = 0 \qquad\qquad x^2 + 5x - 2 = 0$$

$$3(-2)^2 + 5(-2) - 2 \stackrel{?}{=} 0 \qquad\qquad 3(\tfrac{1}{3})^2 + 5(\tfrac{1}{3}) - 2 \stackrel{?}{=} 0$$

$$3(4) + 5(-2) - 2 \stackrel{?}{=} 0 \qquad\qquad 3(\tfrac{1}{9}) + 5(\tfrac{1}{3}) - 2 \stackrel{?}{=} 0$$

$$12 - 10 - 2 = 0 \qquad\qquad \frac{1}{3} + \frac{5}{3} - 2 = 0$$

Applying the complete-the-square method to the general quadratic equation $ax^2 + bx + c = 0$ gives its solutions in terms of the coefficients a, b, and c, which can be used as a formula for solving any quadratic equation.

Visualize the two sides of the equation as equal areas.

ax^2 $\frac{1}{2}bx$	
$\frac{1}{2}bx$ c	

$$= \quad 0 \qquad\qquad ax^2 + bx + c = 0$$

Area Model   Algebraic Record

1. Apply the Zero Principle.

$$ax^2 \quad \frac{1}{2}bx \qquad = \quad -c \qquad\qquad ax^2 + bx = -c$$

$$\frac{1}{2}bx$$

2. Complete the square.

 $\Big\}\sqrt{a}x$

The area of each rectangular region is $\frac{b}{2}x$. Consider its dimensions.

Since $(\sqrt{a}x)(?) = \frac{b}{2}x$, the width of the rectangular region must be $\frac{b}{2\sqrt{a}}$.

Thus, the area that must be added to complete the square is $\frac{b^2}{4a}$.

$$ax^2 \quad \frac{1}{2}bx \qquad = \quad \frac{b^2}{4a} - c \qquad\qquad ax^2 + bx + \frac{b^2}{4a} = \frac{b^2}{4a} - c$$

$$\frac{1}{2}bx \quad \frac{b^2}{4a}$$

3. Determine the dimensions of each square. Equate the dimensions.

$$\sqrt{a}x + \frac{b}{2\sqrt{a}} \qquad \sqrt{\frac{b^2}{4a} - c} \text{ or } -\sqrt{\frac{b^2}{4a} - c}$$

$$ax^2 \quad \frac{1}{2}bx \qquad = \quad \frac{b^2}{4a} - c \qquad\qquad \sqrt{a}x + \frac{b}{2\sqrt{a}} = \pm\sqrt{\frac{b^2}{4a} - c}$$

$$\frac{1}{2}bx \quad \frac{b^2}{4a}$$

Solve for x.

$$\sqrt{a}x + \frac{b}{2\sqrt{a}} = \pm\sqrt{\frac{b^2}{4a} - c}$$

$$\sqrt{a}x = -\frac{b}{2\sqrt{a}} \pm \sqrt{\frac{b^2}{4a} - c}$$

$$\sqrt{a}x = -\frac{b}{2\sqrt{a}} \pm \frac{\sqrt{b^2 - 4ac}}{2\sqrt{a}}$$

$$\sqrt{a}x = \frac{-b \pm \sqrt{b^2 - 4ac}}{2\sqrt{a}}$$

$$x = \frac{-b \pm \sqrt{b^2 - 4ac}}{2a}$$

Quadratic Formula

If $ax^2 + bx + c = 0$ $(a \neq 0)$, then $x = \dfrac{-b \pm \sqrt{b^2 - 4ac}}{2a}$

Note: You may wish to contrast the method of completing the square for solving quadratic equations with the factoring method by visualizing both as equating equal areas and considering why the rectangular region in the factor model must be equated to a region whose area is zero. For example, consider why each dimension in the tile model of $2x^2 + x - 6 = 0$ is equated with zero.

That is, in order for the area of a rectangle to be zero, either of its dimensions must be zero.

REINFORCEMENT

1. From your textbook, select several quadratic equations stated in the form $y = ax^2 + bx + c = 0$, in which a is 1 and b is an even number. Have the students model the steps in the complete-the-square solution method with tiles or drawings.
2. Verify the solutions found in Exercise 1 by applying the quadratic formula.

ASSIGNMENT

1. As students use the completing-the-square method to solve quadratic equations selected from your textbook, have them illustrate the process with an area model.

2. Select which of the three methods — factoring, completing the square, or applying the quadratic formula — you think is most efficient for solving each of the following quadratic equations and explain your reasoning.

   a. $x^2 + 8x + 16 = 0$ b. $x^2 + 6x + 8 = 0$ c. $4x^2 + 12x + 9 = 0$
   d. $5x^2 + x - 2 = 0$ e. $x^2 + 4x - 5 = 0$ f. $2x^2 + x - 1 = 0$

EXTENSION (Optional)

1. Use Base Ten Blocks or Metric Blocks to explore the extension of completing the square to completing the cube.

   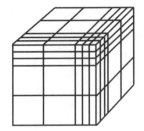

$(x+1)^3 = x^3 + 3x^2 + 3x + 1$ $(2x + 3)^3 = 8x^3 + 36x^2 + 54x + 27$

Investigate how the numbers of each type of three dimensional region impact each other and how the coefficients in the expanded form $ax^3 + bx^2 + cx + d$ are related.

Note: You may wish to suggest that, in exploring the relationship of the coefficients of the general cubic expression, interested students compare them with the coefficients of the terms in the expanded form of $(\sqrt[3]{a} + \sqrt[3]{b})^3$. It is these relationships, generally expressed in parametric form, that make the computation so messy when expressing formulas for solving general cubic and quadratic equations.

---

2. The method of solving quadratic equations by completing the square has been known since Babylonian times. The history of attempts to solve general equations of order greater than two, such as the cubic and quadratic equations ($ax^3 + bx^2 + cx + d = 0$ and $ax^4 + bx^3 + cx^2 + dx + e = 0$) include accounts of competition and intrigue among some of the greatest mathematicians of their day. James Gregory (1638-75), in connection with his work on integration, surmised that one could not solve algebraically the general nth-degree equation for $n > 4$. Do some research on these attempts that contributed significantly in a branch of mathematics called *theory of equations*.

MORE THINKING ABOUT AREA MODELS

Throughout history, there have been a variety of methods for determining the product of two numbers. Several can be represented with area models.

The Lightning Method, for example, can be represented as an area model.

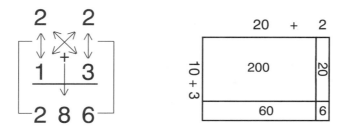

The Quarter Squares Method, used in the late 17th through early 19th centuries, is based on the relationship,

$$ab = \frac{(a + b)^2}{4} - \frac{(a - b)^2}{4}$$

which, when expressed as $4ab = (a + b)^2 - (a - b)^2$, can be represented by an area model that holds for any real-number values of a and b.

The Quarter Squares Method utilizes the quarter square (QS) table.

n	0	1	2	3	4	5	6	7	8
QS_n	0	0	1	2	4	6	9	12	16
9	10	11	12	13	14	15	16	17	18
20	25	30	36	42	49	56	64	72	81
19	20	21	22	23	24	25	26	27	28
90	100	110	121	132	144	156	169	182	196
29	30	31	32	33	34	35	36	37	38
210	225	240	256	272	289	306	324	342	361
39	40	41	42	43	44	45	46	47	48
380	400	420	441	462	484	506	529	552	576

To multiply 22 by 13, subtract the QS of their differences from the QS of their sum.

$$22 + 13 = 35 \quad \text{QS } 306$$
$$22 - 13 = 9 \quad \text{QS } \underline{20}$$
$$286$$

Students should realize that the Quarter Squares Method was popular before the invention of convenient mechanical devices eliminated the drudgery of multiplying large numbers. The extensive

Quarter Squares tables made it possible to multiply large numbers quickly and easily.

You may wish to suggest that students verify and extend the table entries, and explain how this Algebra Tile representation models the Quarter Squares Method.

$$\left(\begin{array}{|c|c|} \hline a^2 & ab \\ \hline ab & b^2 \\ \hline \end{array} \right) - \left(\begin{array}{|c|c|} \hline a^2 & -ab \\ \hline -ab & b^2 \\ \hline \end{array} \right) = \boxed{ab}\ \boxed{ab}\ \boxed{ab}\ \boxed{ab}$$

(left square labeled $a+b$ on top and $a+b$ on side; right square labeled $a-b$ on top and $a-b$ on side)

Interested students may wish to explore these methods to deepen their appreciation of the connections between algebra and geometry.